ICE SURPRISE

Contents

Rusty and the Ice-Cream  page 2

Revolting Ice-Creams page 14

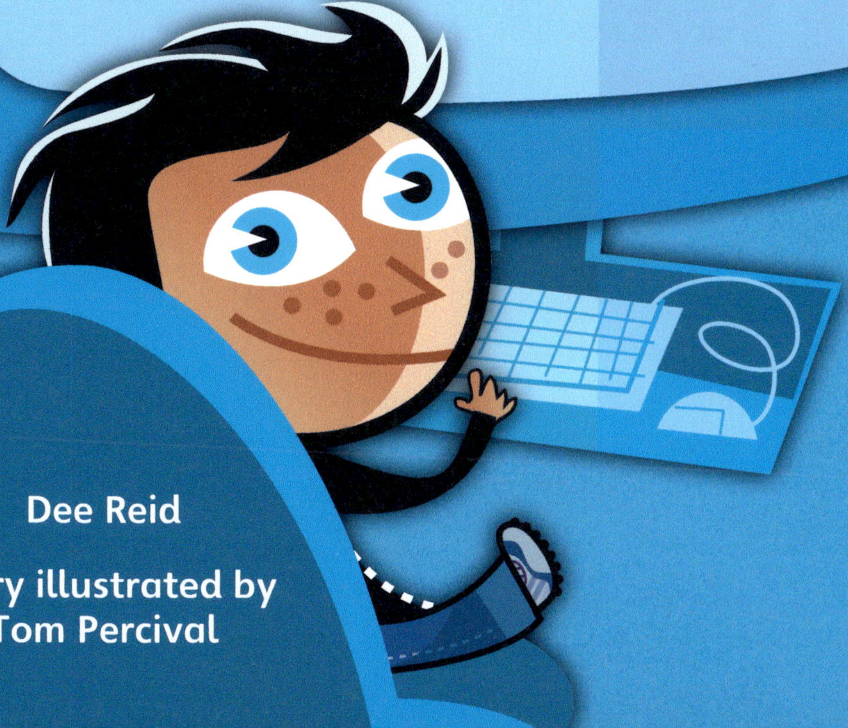

Dee Reid

Story illustrated by Tom Percival

Before Reading

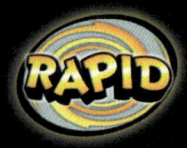

In this story

 Rusty

 The ice-cream man

 Some children

Tricky words

- ice-cream
- scooped
- more
- children

Introduce these tricky words and help the reader when they come across them later!

Story starter

Rusty is a robot. He is old and rusty but he likes to help people. One day, Rusty wanted an ice-cream but he had to wait in a big queue.

Rusty and the Ice-Cream

"Can I have an ice-cream?" said Rusty.

"You can have an ice-cream," said the man.
"But can you help me?"

"I can help you," said Rusty.

Rusty scooped the ice-cream.

Rusty scooped and scooped.

What do you think will happen next?

Rusty scooped more and more ice-cream.

"Stop! Stop!" said the man.

"You rusty tin can," said the man. "You have scooped all the ice-cream."

"But I can help you," said Rusty.

Quiz

Text Detective

- Why did the children like Rusty helping the ice-cream man?
- Do you think Rusty was a big help in the end?

Word Detective

- **Phonic Focus:** Initial phonemes
  Page 5: Find a word beginning with the phoneme 'h'.
- Page 9: How many syllables are there in the word 'children'?
- Page 10: Find a word that rhymes with 'pin'.

Super Speller

Read this word:

an

Now try to spell it!

HA! HA! HA!

Q Who serves ice-cream faster than a speeding bullet?

 Scooperman!

Before Reading

Find out about

- All the different flavours of ice-cream you can buy

Tricky words

- people
- strawberry
- cheese
- chocolate
- pasta
- mustard
- vanilla

Introduce these tricky words and help the reader when they come across them later!

Text starter

Some people like to eat ice-cream, but did you know that there are some unusual ice-cream flavours? Would you eat cheese ice-cream, or pasta, or mustard, or fish ice-cream?

Revolting Ice-Creams

Some people like to eat ice-cream.

Some people like strawberry ice-cream.

What is your favourite flavour of ice-cream?

This ice-cream is made of cheese.

Would you eat this ice-cream?

Some people like chocolate ice-cream.

This ice-cream is made of pasta.

Would you eat this ice-cream?

Some people like mint chocolate ice-cream.

This ice-cream is made of mustard.

Would you eat this ice-cream?

Some people like vanilla ice-cream.

This ice-cream is made of fish!

Would you eat this ice-cream?

Quiz

Text Detective

- What flavour ice-creams do some people like?
- Which flavour of ice-cream do you think sounds revolting?

Word Detective

- **Phonic Focus:** Initial phonemes
  Page 15: Find a word beginning with the phoneme 'l'.
- Page 16: Find a word that rhymes with 'bike'.
- Page 19: Can you find a small word inside the word 'made'?

Super Speller

Read this word:

to

Now try to spell it!

HA! HA! HA!

Q Which fish goes well with ice-cream?

A Jellyfish.